RC AJUONUMA enjoys dream
writing them down. He also lik
ball, but not necessarily in tha
London with his family.

King Billy
and the
Royal Road

RC Ajuonuma

SilverWood

Published in 2017 by SilverWood Books

SilverWood Books Ltd
14 Small Street, Bristol, BS1 1DE, United Kingdom
www.silverwoodbooks.co.uk

Copyright © RC Ajuonuma 2017
Images © Beverley Young 2017

The right of RC Ajuonuma to be identified as the author of
this work has been asserted in accordance with the Copyright,
Designs and Patents Act 1988 Sections 77 and 78.

ISBN 978-1-78132-704-3 (paperback)
ISBN 978-1-78132-705-0 (ebook)

British Library Cataloguing in Publication Data
A CIP catalogue record for this book is available from
the British Library

Page design and typesetting by SilverWood Books
Printed on responsibly sourced paper

For my son

Part 1

The Way to Your Heart

1

A trumpet blew loud,
like a call from a cloud,
and Billy awoke with a start!

He looked overhead,
then under his bed,
in search of the source of the blast.

Baffled and stumped,
he mumbled and shrugged,
and stretched like a cat on a beach.

Then he noticed a whiff,
of candy and crisps,
and drooled and sprang out from his sheets!

The smell was so yummy,
it toyed with his tummy
until he felt starved as a pig.

He crept 'cross the floor,
as his mum gently snored,
and made his way straight for the fridge.

He opened it up,
then whined like a pup,
as the shelves were all barren and bare.

"But how could this be?
It's NEVER empty!"
he cried, and ran back up the stairs.

He burst in the room,
where his mum was a-snooze,
in snivels and sniffles and snot.

"Your brave little prince,"
he said with a wince,
"is so hungry his belly's in knots!"

He shoved and he shook,
as hard as he could,
but she wouldn't wake up from her doze.

Keen not to be stuck
with a gurgling gut,
he dashed off to put on some clothes.

Then he snatched at a sack,
which was stuffed in a rack,
and a stick that was slung on the ground

by his mum, on the day
when she last came away
with a bag full of treats from the town.

Billy strode to the door,
then stopped just before,
and started to shake with a fear,

as he'd never been past
his mother's front yard,
and didn't quite know what was there.

He stepped on the porch,
with the scariest thoughts,
then faced a mad dog by the gate,

which his mother had said
was his very best friend
each time he'd asked for a mate.

Billy gulped, and he snuck
by the growling gruff mutt,
as it yanked and pulled on its chain.

He looked back at the house,
with his heart in his mouth,
and made his way off down the lane.

2

He walked in the warmth
of a bright summer dawn
till he came to a place by a cove

where a man in a hat
with a cape and a tan
was sprawled on a chair by a stove.

He breathed in the smell
of fish from a shell
in a sizzling, spluttering pan

and, trying his luck,
Billy tiptoed on up,
and spoke to the top-hatted man.

"Excuse me, dear sir,
do stay as you were,
but is there enough there for two?

I'm so horribly starved,
and I'm sure I'm too far
from a shop that would serve me some food."

The sun-covered cook
had a very long look
at the boy with the stick in his hand.

"I think that you might
be the travelling type!"
he pronounced, with a flourish so grand.

"Let me make you a deal,
because that's how I feel.
I'm sure that you'll be very pleased.

If you give me that stick,
and your rucksack with it,
I'll give you the thing that you need."

Hungry to eat
either snacks or a treat,
Billy gave the strange man what he sought.

He opened the bag,
which he wiggled and wagged,
and pulled from inside an old sword.

Then he gave it a whack,
and from out of the pack,
came a coin and an old-fashioned cup.

He took Billy's staff,
with a hearty great laugh,
and swung it around like a club!

"I really can't think
how a brave little prince
such as I could've carried such junk.

15

But you're welcome to it
if it lifts your spirit!
It's food that I want…and love."

"Things are more than they seem,"
said the man with the gleam,
"but you're right – let's not make such a fuss."

He reached in the cape
that hung from his nape,
and pulled out a shining atlas.

"Is this some kind of tease?"
asked Billy, displeased.
"That really is not what you owe."

"It's the world in a read,"
said the man, eagerly.
"It'll show you which places to go."

Billy rushed to the hob,
then started to sob,
as the food was now blackened and charred.

"You tricked me!" he said,
"and now I'm unfed.
You caught me when I was off-guard!"

"Relax, my dear chap,
and take up your map,
so you can see all of the globe."

Billy's pride was so stung,
he stuck out his tongue,
and stomped away back down the road.

3

He walked for a stretch,
then came to the edge
of a glistening, shimmering wood

where he noticed the whiff
of candy and crisps,
and everything else that was good.

The smell was so yummy,
it toyed with his tummy
until he felt starved as a horse.

So he ran through the trees
with gold-coloured leaves
and branches quite crooked and coarse,

till he came to a stop
by a shabby sweet shop
that stood all alone in a glade

where, unseen and unstirred,
a little cat purred
on a deck in the cool of the shade.

He opened the door,
but inside it he saw
the shelves were all barren and bare.

And lost in a dream,
sitting high on a beam,
was a woman with curls in her hair.

Her eyes were like glass
that winked in the dark
when the moon showered down its kind light.

And her hand held a book
that had a strange look,
and seemed to grow ever more bright.

"Excuse me, dear ma'am,"
he spoke, with great charm,
"I thought you were selling some treats."

"They're locked in my crypt
with all my secrets!"
she teased, as she swayed in her seat.

"Though I might just relent
if you'd tell me the length
of the whole of the Great China Wall."

"I don't know what that is,
or care for your quiz,
but I think we can settle this all.

I'm a prince in these parts,
and I'm sure if you ask,
there'll be plenty of cash for your till.

So just give me a crate
of your chocolate and cake,
and send someone round with the bill."

With a glow and a gleam,
she dropped from her beam,
and went to kneel down by his side.

"You say you're a prince,
but you're not what you think,"
she said, staring deep in his eyes.

"I know who I am!"
he said, but his hands
seemed to shake with the weight of her gaze.

"Search on the path
for the way to your heart,"
she said, and he left in a daze.

4

Billy sat on a rock,
and tried to take stock
of the strange woman's weird little words,

and asked why a mum
makes a prince of a son
if that isn't what he's worth.

He mulled and mused,
and pondered and chewed,
over what kind of boy he could be,

when it came in a flash –
as sudden as that! –
and crystally clear as the sea.

"The king must be dead
and buried," he said.
"She must've been giving a sign

that the man at the top
has come to a stop
and left me the next in line."

"Now *I* am the king!"
He smirked and he grinned,
then sniggered and made a big snort.

But his triumph and joy
only served to annoy
a passing duchess and her court.

"Young man, you're too loud.
You offend with this sound!"
she brayed as she stopped her grand march.

"Hush!" he decreed.
"And show your esteem,
for I've got the realm in my charge!"

"Frankly, my dear,"
she drawled from her chair,
"I'd say you're just talking rot."

But he gave her a wave,
so regally made,
she spluttered aghast and agog:

"But if you're a tsar
you should look like you are!
You'll get no respect in disguise.

I've ermine and satin
and jewels in my cabin –
each one a great feast for the eye."

Billy climbed from the rock,
chose a robe and frock,
and a crown that he wore as his own.

Then strode to his fort,
leaving duchess and court
in awe as he sat on his throne.

"All hail His Highness,
whose reign is the finest!"
she cried, with a blush on her face.

"Please, grant us our leave,
as I'm sure you must be
overwhelmed with affairs of the state!"

The king gave a nod,
and onward she trod,
with her servants and soldiers in tow.

Billy watched their retreat,
then wished for some sweets.
And they fell from the sky like snow.

But after a time,
a priest of some kind
came by the young king on the rock,

and fell from his bike
at the curious sight
of the sovereign smashing a clock!

"Would you like a large piece
of a chocolate-filled feast?"
Billy asked as the dial spun and swirled.

"Or perhaps just a bite
of some Turkish delight
now we've got all the time in the world!"

The preacher refused
and was far from amused,
as Billy ate plate after plate:

"This is gluttony, sire;
you'll burn in the fire
and have such a bad belly ache!"

"I can do what I please!"
cried Billy the liege,
"because what I want will just happen!

I could wish on a star
for a bike or a car
or a ship I could blast off to Saturn!"

"This is vanity, sire;
you'll burn in the fire!"
the priest warned with such sombre relish.

"Well, by then, sir, at least,
you'll have left me in peace!"
said the king, and the priest promptly vanished!

Billy raised up a toast
to the minister's ghost,
but as soon as the drink passed his lips

his bottomless belly
wobbled like jelly,
and then he began to feel sick.

"Oh, it really is cruel
to be so overfull,"
said Billy, quite sticky and glum.

And he groaned as the sound
of a merry-go-round
rang out from his poor little tum.

He crawled from his throne,
as stiff as a stone,
straight up to a fork in the way:

to the left was a lane
that was rough and unpaved,
while the right said: 'ten miles to sickbay'.

So, feeling much worse,
he made for the nurse,
but then he was struck by the sight

of a girl so divine,
with a marigold smile,
whose eyes fired off their own light!

"Do you know me?" she asked,
then giggled and laughed.
"I'm the friend that you never have seen.

All the days you were sad,
and feeling so bad,
you were never alone, as it seemed.

But now is the time
for the churches to chime,
and a bride to be wed to her groom.

Walk with me a while
down this narrow dirt aisle.
There's someone who's waiting for you."

Billy's heart missed a beat,
and his soul simply beamed
as she smiled and led him by the hand

down the lane to the left –
that was rough and unkept –
as the king and the queen of the land.

"I was sore and unwell,"
Billy said to his belle.
"But now I could guzzle again!"

The girl with the smile
looked sad for a while,
then left just as quick as she came.

Part 2

Be Brave, Be True

5

Billy awoke
with a cough and a croak,
then let out the deepest of sighs.

He yanked on a bell,
with a scream and a yell,
and a maid scurried in with some pies.

"Is this some kind of joke?"
he more spluttered than spoke,
then rose to slump down on a chair.

"Forgive me, my liege.
I thought you'd be pleased –
I really was quite unaware."

"I am done with this food!"
he barked, in a mood,
then gave all the pies a good kick.

"I really must find
my beautiful bride,
or else I'll be blue and heartsick.

So prepare me a mount!
It's time I went out
to hunt high and low for my queen."

"My lord, it's a shame,
but your horse is now lame,"
said the maid as she scrubbed the floor clean.

"Then I'll search in my jet
till the day's sun is set!"
said Billy, quite surly and smug.

"The last time I looked,
your plane was kaput!"
she said, clearing crumbs from a rug.

"I wished for a tower
to grow like a flower –
a plane will be easy to fix!"

So he strode out with pride,
but to his surprise,
the jet was still broken in bits.

"How very strange!"
said the little king's maid,
as they stood in his castle's great yard.

"Enough of such talk –
I simply will walk!"
he cried, storming past the gate guards.

Some way from his camp,
he came by a tramp
with a face that was covered in sores.

"Could you spare me some change?"
said the wretch, half ashamed.
"I really won't ask you for more."

"You pest!" Billy snapped,
as he pushed past the tramp.
"Don't bore me with tales of your woe.

"I'm in search of a girl
with a marigold twirl,
and eyes that give off their own glow!"

"I knew such a lass,"
said the wretch, "but alas,
she is gone, though I searched far and wide."

"Say of whom you do speak!"
Billy barked in a pique.
"What news do you have of my bride?"

"Well, the girl that I knew
had a daisy-like hue
and her eyes shone a flame and a flare.

All the days I was sad,
and feeling so bad,
though I seemed on my own, she was there.

But I cared just for me,
so I never did see
whom it was she'd wanted to show.

I got cruel and confused.
No more wishes came true.
And I ended up lost and alone."

Now, Billy went pale
at the tell of this tale,
and wondered if here was a sight

of the way people scar
when they think that they are
all that counts when they live out a life.

"It feels awful to make
such a silly mistake –
how could I be rich if you suffer?"

So he gave up his gold
to the vagabond soul,
who hugged him as tight as a brother.

6

Billy took to the road
with a smile as he roamed
through a fog that billowed and grew.

Then he heard the faint sound
of a bark and growl,
and glimpsed the most terrible view.

From out of the mist,
with a snarl and hiss,
came the scariest, eeriest hound,

which his mother had said
was a much better friend
than the boys and girls in the town.

He trembled in fear
as it raced ever near,
with a broken chain trailing behind.

Before it could pounce,
with a scream and a shout,
he raced away till he arrived

at the mouth of a cave
that was dark as a grave,
but the dog was still near, he was sure.

So, he followed it down,
all the way underground,
till he stumbled upon an old door

that was set in the rock
with a key in its lock,
and opened up on to a room

where a lamp burned low
on a table of stone
that curved like a crescent-shaped moon.

By the light was a book
that had a strange look,
like the one the weird woman read.

"Be brave, be true.
And your heart will find you,"
was all that each page simply said.

He put down the book.
Then at once, the cave shook.
And the light of the world flooded in.

He peered through the dust,
and saw he was thrust
at the foot of a mega mountain!

He scaled the steep rock
on a path to the top,
where he caught the most dazzling sight

of a circling wheel,
made of diamonds and steel,
that reached a magnificent height!

And there in a stall –
at the foot of it all –
was a man in the tallest of hats

with a billowing cape,
which hung from his nape,
and a face that shone with a tan.

"I've seen you before!"
Billy shouted. "I'm sure
you're the man who made all the food burn!"

"And you must be the chap
who threw out the atlas –
what brings you to the top of the world?"

"Can you do me a deal
for a turn on the wheel?
I really must go for a spin!"

"Well, to see all the Earth
from so lofty a perch
is worth the full price of a king."

"How much would that be?"
he asked warily.
"Is it something I could just owe?"

"You don't pay in advance.
And as far as the charge,
you never do really quite know."

Billy felt in a fix –
though he longed for the trip –
as the terms didn't really appeal.

But watching it whirl
with a swish and a swirl,
he knew he must go on that wheel!

So he ran to the ride,
which lifted him high,
to twirl in the wisps of the clouds.

He rolled and spun,
and watched as the sun
shone out, with its rays flooding down

on deserts and seas,
oceans and trees,
and everything seemed to just glow

as he gazed at the view,
with its green and blue,
and the joy in his heart overflowed.

7

Billy sat on a beach
at the foot of the peak
and marvelled at what he'd seen:

such a sight as the world
in a glorious twirl
was a thing to be shared with his queen!

He looked to the sea,
and stood as the breeze
blew soft like the fur on a foal,

and wondered what wind
he could beckon to bring
him the scent of his bright Marigold.

Then out of his thoughts
he was roused by a horse
that trotted along up ahead,

pulling hard on a cart
at the front of a march
of a court and its passing duchess.

"Your Highness!" she brayed,
and paused her parade.
"Forgive me the tale that I tell,

but a man in a hat
with a cape at his back
has said that your mother's unwell."

"That can't be right,"
he said, in a fright.
"My mum's as fit as a flea."

"I wish it were so,"
she said, with some woe.
"It's best if you went back to see."

"This is out of the blue –
are you sure it's true?"
he asked, quite torn and perplexed.

"If it's only a cold
that's taken its hold,
I'd rather continue my quest."

"It's more than a chill –
he told me she's ill!
And has been since you wandered off!

But of course, it's your right
to do as you like."
And on with her troop she trod.

Billy sat on the beach
at the foot of the peak,
with a mist and a tear in his eye.

He pictured his mum
all alone with no one
by her side and so sick she could die.

Then he thought of the girl
with the marigold twirl
and eyes that gave off their own glow,

with her smile and shine
and spark, so divine,
and secrets she wanted to show.

He couldn't decide:
his mum or his bride?
The joy in his heart turned to pain.

And he curled in the dust
till the day turned to dusk,
and a top-hatted man slowly came.

"Do you know me?" he asked
from behind a skull mask.
"I am no respecter of kings.

And it must now be so
that you pay what you owe
for the sight of the world in a spin."

Billy sat on the beach
at the foot of the peak,
and shivered and shuddered with dread.

Then the man in the cloak
pulled a blade, at a stroke,
and deprived the great king of his head.

Part 3

What Was Lost Can Be Found

8

The girl with the marigold
smile sat down
on the ground where she found the king slain.

With both hands, she stretched
to pick up the royal head,
which was cold and covered with stains.

She cleansed his face,
and removed all trace
of the dirt, the blood and the sand.

Then she crept to the corpse
that was hunched on the floor,
and wished it and willed it to stand.

With hands glowing red
round the king's severed head,
she lifted it up like a crown.

Then spoke out the words
she longed to be heard,
as she brought Billy's brow slowly down:

"When you stood on the mount,
from the wheel looking out,
you saw all the world as I do.

When a point on a map
is no more than just that,
you'll know what it means to be you."

She gave him a kiss,
which fizzled with bliss,
and healed every bone from its break.

Then with naught but a wink,
she was gone in a blink,
and Billy sprang up wide awake!

He looked all around,
unsure of his ground
and whether he lived or was dead.

Then he felt such a breeze
that blew from the sea
and picked up the sweetest of scents,

of a girl so divine
with a marigold smile,
who wasn't so very far-flung.

So he took to the road,
but was gripped by a groan
from his gurgling, murmuring tum.

He walked for a stretch,
then came to the edge
of a grimacing, glowering wood

where he noticed the whiff
of candy and crisps,
and everything else that was good.

The smell was so yummy,
it toyed with his tummy
until he was starving and sick.

So he raced through the trees
with dark-coloured leaves
and branches misshapen and thick,

till he came to a heap
of the tastiest treats,
and a monster that belched as it fed

with the legs of a goat
and the stink of a stoat,
and a horn on each side of its head.

"Would you like a big piece
of a chocolate-filled feast?"
it asked as it lurked and prowled.

"Or perhaps just a bite
of some Turkish delight –
there's so much of the stuff to go round!"

Billy flinched in fright
at the perilous sight
of the beast as it bared its sharp teeth.

But being so near
to a chocolate éclair,
his belly grew desperate to eat.

"I've treacle and sherbet,
and chips and cheeseburgers,"
the monster said, licking its lips.

"And plump chicken thighs
and freshly baked pies,
and everything else you could wish!"

Billy's gut gave a growl
that turned to a howl,
and he knew that he couldn't refuse.

So he leapt on the heap
of the tastiest treats,
so squishy and squashy they oozed.

He ate to the last
of the raspberry tarts;
then gorged on a party of cakes.

And when they were gone,
he turned to the scones
and ate them all up in a haste!

But as soon as he'd come
to the crunchiest crumb,
he burped and began to be ill.

The beast gave a laugh
from the stone in its heart,
and rolled all around in the swill.

Billy felt so ashamed
he'd guzzled again
he dashed away into the night,

and shivered with cold
as a thundercloud rolled
and the trees and the wind had a fight.

He wondered what curse
or spell or much worse
had pulled him from palace and throne

to search for a girl
with a marigold twirl,
and wander so lost and alone.

In the swirl of the rain,
he wished and prayed
for a place to shelter close by.

Then he glimpsed, through the storm,
his castle's grand wall –
its tower raised up to the sky!

He screamed with relief
at the sight of his seat
and raced to the fortress ahead,

with its jewels and cars
and troops standing guard,
and servants who tucked him in bed.

But swelling with pride
at the riches inside,
he tripped and was zapped by a light,

as a bolt from the blue
(with an aim good and true)
struck down the great fort with such might!

When he opened his eyes,
he sobbed and he cried
at what had become of his throne,

as the glorious tower
that grew like a flower
was now just a jumble of stones.

9

He staggered away
from the rubble and came
to the glint and glow of a lake,

which reflected an arc
of a thousand bright sparks
that criss-crossed the sky like snowflakes.

The night was now still,
and the lake had the feel
of a place where the weary could rest,

and the heavy could hope
to lie and unload
and float to the light up ahead.

Billy peeled off his clothes,
then dipped a big toe
in the lake, and watched as it twirled.

Then sank in his feet,
and waded in deep
until he was soaked in the swirl.

He sat by the side
of the lake as he dried,
and thought of his time on the road:

the things he'd seen,
the places he'd been –
but now he just longed for his home.

Then out of the night,
in a shimmering light,
came the girl with an air so divine.

Her eyes held a spark
of a flame in the dark,
and her face shone a marigold smile.

"Where have you been?"
he asked of his queen.
"Waiting here for you," she said.

"I don't care for this throne.
I just want to go home,
and be with my mum by her bed."

The girl with the smile
grew sad for a while,
and sat with the king by the lake.

"I'm so sorry," she sighed,
"but your mother has died."
And he felt that his heart would just break.

"I shouldn't have left!"
he screamed and wept.
"And now I don't know what to do!"

The girl with the glow
knew the pain and the woe,
as he cried and sobbed with him too.

"There's a place on the path
where the wish of your heart
is shown by a bird and a beast.

And curled in the grace
of that well-buried place,
you'll find all the answers you seek."

She showed him a way
through a wood to a glade,
where Billy could make out the sight

of a shop full of sweets
and the tastiest treats,
and a woman who waited outside.

Her eyes were like glass
that winked in the dark
when the moon showered down its kind light.

And her hand held a book
that had a strange look,
and seemed to grow ever more bright.

Billy gazed at the scene,
with its glimmer and gleam,
and knew that to there he must go.

He walked through the trees
with gold-coloured leaves
and branches that blew to and fro

till he came to the shop
where he found she was not
at her seat by the cat on the porch.

He tiptoed inside,
and followed the signs
that glowed in the dark like a torch

all the way till he found
a hole in the ground,
and stopped to draw in a deep breath.

Then tumbled inside,
with arms open wide
and heart beating loud in his chest.

10

He crashed in a heap
of the tastiest treats
piled high on a stone cellar floor,

and saw to his shock
that the stack was the stock
of the food from his mother's own store!

But he had little wish
for a snack or a dish,
so he walked further into the crypt.

And saw in a nook
the weird woman's book,
which glowed with a light from its script.

"What was lost can be found,
in the world underground,"
was all that each page simply said.

Billy peered through the gloom
in the dark of the tomb,
and glimpsed an old door up ahead.

He left the great heap
of the tastiest treats,
and strode from the dim to a night

that was lit by the moon,
which swelled in a swoon
like a mother who held a new life.

He walked in a mist,
which whispered and hissed,
and tried to make out a clear path,

but this world was a haze
and his wits in a daze
at what in the fog could be masked.

Then out of the murk –
where the monsters lurk –
there came the most miserable sound.

And the mist and haze
gave way to a cage
with a beast that was slumped on the ground.

Its legs were a goat's
and it stank of a stoat,
with a horn on each side of its head.

And perched on its brow
was a rusty old crown,
which looked to be heavy as lead.

"Have pity on me
and let me be free!"
the sorry beast whimpered and moaned.

"I miss the green fields
and valleys and hills!"
it said, and let out a groan.

Billy shook like a leaf,
and prayed the beast
wouldn't break out and tear him to bits.

"You're ugly and cruel!"
he yelled at the ghoul.
"You laughed when the food made me sick!"

"I get very starved
when I'm stuck behind bars,"
the monster said, gloomy and blue.

"If I only could run,
you'd eat just for one
and no longer tuck in for two!"

"But what do you mean?"
he asked of the fiend.
"Why make me a part of your tale?"

"If you don't let me out,
you'll be stuffing your mouth
till we're both just a blob in a jail."

Billy stared at the beast
that longed for release,
and felt a great pain in his heart.

He opened the cage
that lay in the shade,
and the creature flew out like a dart.

It let out a shriek
then fell at his feet,
and out of its belly was sprung –

a faun with a grin,
a clean-shaven chin
and eyes full of frolics and fun!

"What became of the beast?"
in such disbelief,
he asked, as he stared at the sight

of this gaggle of joy –
half goat and half boy –
that giggled and smirked in the night.

"You're being a yawn!"
said the rascally faun.
"The beast that was here is now gone!

And I'd suggest
it would really be best
to forget him and hurry along!"

"But where should I go?
Do you happen to know?
I can't find the way for the fog."

"Walk right, then left!"
said the faun, in a jest,
and then, with a wink, it was gone.

11

Billy roamed through the haze
and mist-covered maze
until he was hopelessly lost.

Without any clue
as to what he should do,
he wept in the fog and the frost.

He sobbed and sighed,
as his feverish mind
was flooded with visions of fools

who journeyed alone,
away from their homes,
to wander this land full of ghouls.

He looked to the moon,
and remembered a tune
his mum used to sing when he cried:

"Don't weep, little one,
just think of the sun
when you wake in the dark of the night."

As he wiped off a tear,
he thought he could hear
the sound of his mother's soft voice

floating out of the haze,
like a ghost from a grave
that had come to the end of its voyage.

He dashed to and fro,
so desperate to know
just what he'd heard in the fog.

Then out of the mist,
with a snarl and hiss,
came the scariest, eeriest dog,

which his mother had said
was his very best friend
each time he'd asked for a mate.

It barked and growled
and circled around,
and he shuddered with dread as it paced.

But the longer he looked,
the less he shook
and the more he was hurt in his heart

by the sight of the hound
his mother had found
to keep him at home and hearth.

He glared at the brute
full of bruises and wounds,
and anger that turned to a rage.

"Leave me alone!"
he yelled from his bones.
It yelped and then scurried away.

Then out of the haze
came a woman who gazed
at Billy with tears in her eyes.

He couldn't believe
what it was he could see,
as his mother knelt down by his side:

"The world is a place
where no one is safe.
It's full of such sorrow and grief.

I kept it away
and left you to play,
and hoped that your life would be sweet."

"But how can I grow
if you won't let me go?"
he asked, so sad, as he cried.

"I can't be a king
if I don't know a thing
of life in the world outside!"

"Now you've seen what it is,
my brave little prince,
why don't you just stay here with me?"

"I love you so much,"
he sobbed, as they touched,
"but now you must let me be free..."

The glimmering ghost
drew Billy in close
and gave him a sorrowful kiss.

She clung to him tight,
wailed in the night,
then faded away in the mist.

12

Billy sat very still,
then summoned his will,
and the fog rose to unveil a shore

where a lion, so proud,
with its mane blowing round,
let out the most powerful *roar*!

Then out of the sea,
with her eyes all a-gleam,
came the weird woman dressed in blue robes,

with her beasts and birds,
chanting beautiful words
said in hushed and mysterious tones.

She showed him a boat
that was moored on the coast,
and Billy walked up and got in.

Then he lay on the floor
of the boat by the shore,
and purred as it rocked in the wind.

He drew in a breath,
and from out of his chest
a long-buried lark flew away.

And the sound of its song
sent the boat sailing on
from the night of the moon to the day.

13

The sun blazed a fire
above the wrecked tower
where Billy curled up, with a smile.

He gazed and swooned
at the flowers that bloomed
from the ash of the tumbledown pile.

A baby rode forth
on a gallant white horse
with a glittering crown on its head.

Then it came to a stop
by the flowers and rocks,
and jumped as if sprung from a bed.

"What's your name? Do you fly?"
asked the boy, bouncing by.
"Do you know why the sky is so tall?

"Have you been on a trip?
Do you know how to skip
down the whole of the great China Wall?"

Then he grabbed at a stone,
which he gave a good blow,
and it turned to a glowing red ball.

And he threw it to Billy,
who beamed like this really
was just the best game of them all!

To this happiest scene,
his sparkling queen
was brought by a silk parachute

in a white wedding dress,
though he couldn't quite guess
why a trumpet was tied to her shoe.

She smiled at the sight
of the child glowing bright
who placed on the king the great crown,

and said as the two
played royal peekaboo
in meadows that grew all around:

"He knows you're home
wherever you roam –
it's the gift that he brings and the start

of a life that's new.
And joyful. And true.
Now you've finally found your heart."

Billy stared at the child,
with his thoughts running wild
and soul overflowing with bliss.

"I want all of the world,"
he said to the girl,
"to know how it feels to be *this*!"

"Well they won't while they snooze,"
she said, and she threw
the brass trumpet straight into his arms.

Billy opened his chest,
took in a deep breath,
and puffed out his cheeks and blew hard!

Then he looked down below
at the shining royal road,
and his heart at the scene skipped a beat

as a gathering crowd,
woken up by a sound,
walked on to a house by a beach

where a top-hatted man
with a cape and tan
will change an old stick and a coin

and a cup and a sword,
from the bags they brought,
to the life that would bring the most joy.

So wish for a cup
that's flowing with love,
and from it your fill you can drink!

Wish for a sword
that sharpens a thought
till it cuts and is clear as the wind!

Wish for a coin
that reminds you're joined
to the treasures that come from the earth!

Wish for a wand
made of fire and song,
and your spirit will burn with an urge

to rise to the clouds,
and dance all around,
like a boy who'd always been free!

"I am the world!"
Billy yelled, as he twirled.
"And the world is the king I'll be."

Lightning Source UK Ltd.
Milton Keynes UK
UKOW04f0635221117
313098UK00001B/218/P